# Christmas in July

**Holly...** has made batches of Winter spice potpourri all summer.

**Mary Elizabeth** ...stamped and stencilled hatboxes to hold lots of little holiday gifts.

**Kate** ...loves eggnog popsicles.

# CHRISTMAS in WHEN?

That's right ··· in JULY!

Spend a few of those lazy, hazy days of summer getting the jump on this year's Christmas list. You'll enjoy it more ∽ less last·minute pressure and more time for inspiration!

So gather a group of friends 'round the pool and brainstorm about Santas, snowmen and Christmas lists... then get together again and again and again all summer long to get a gain on making piles of great little gifts... and you'll be done

# before Santa Claus!

Mañana is often the busiest day of the week.
-SPANISH PROVERB-

# CHRISTMAS in JULY

Get the Girls together
and
EAT, drink, and make
merry Christmas crafts.

MOSTLY EAT, OK?

FIRST THINGS FIRST:

FILL 'EM UP
with
# Santa Claus Pizza

...COOL & LIGHT & TASTES JUST RIGHT...

10·oz. tube pizza crust
8·oz. pkg. cream cheese
1 c. mayonnaise·type salad dressing

½ head lettuce, finely shredded
1 tomato, diced
3·oz. jar bacon bits

Spray a 13"x9" baking pan with non·stick spray; unroll and press crust fit pan. Prick with fork and bake at 425 degrees for 8 to 9 minutes or until golden; cool. Mix cream cheese & dressing until smooth. Spread over crust. Top with lettuce, tomato & bacon. Cut into squares.

# my PARTY PLAN for

# CHRISTMAS in JULY

## I WILL:

...STRING CHRISTMAS LIGHTS OVER THE TABLE WHERE WE'LL BE SITTING.

...DIG OUT A HOLIDAY TABLECLOTH.

...NOT PUT UP THE FULL-FLEDGED CHRISTMAS TREE (OVERKILL, YOU KNOW) BUT I'LL BUY A LITTLE POTTED SPRUCE FOR A CENTERPIECE and PLANT IT OUTSIDE (MINUS DECORATIONS) POST-PARTY.

...PLAY CHRISTMAS CDs WHILE WE "WORK".

...WEAR A SANTA HAT!

...SERVE YUMMY STUFF TO PUT EVERYONE IN THE

# HOLIDAY SPIRIT.

# MARY ELIZABETH'S ONLY ·173· DAYS· LEFT· 'til CHRISTMAS Party Mix

...PERFECT FOR CHOWING DOWN ON A HOT DAY IN JULY.

3 c. BITE·SIZE CORN & RICE CEREAL SQUARES

3 c. BITE·SIZE CRISPY RICE CEREAL SQUARES

3 c. PRETZELS

3 c. BITE·SIZE HONEY CEREAL SQUARES

3 c. NUTS

14·oz. PKG. CANDY·COATED CHOCOLATES

1·3/4 LBS. WHITE MELTING CHOCOLATE, MELTED

*

Combine first six ingredients in a bowl; pour chocolate over top. Stir 'til well-coated. Spread onto wax paper. Cool completely; break apart and store in airtight container. Makes four quarts.

*

...turn up the air conditioner and wash it down with

# Hot COCOA!

(OVER ICE)

5

# Now get busy.

You and your pals can:

Make polka·dot·glitter·spots on frosted glass christmas tree balls ★ Rubber stamp gift tags and rolls of kraft paper for giftwrap ★ Tie up goodies in pretty cello bags or decorate little glass jars for candy stashing ★ Craft wonderful one·of·a· kind Christmas cards ★

... while you chit·chat!

HAVE A QUICK and EASY CRAFT READY TO MAKE AT YOUR CHRISTMAS IN JULY PARTY ～A FAVOR YOUR GUESTS CAN TAKE HOME AS THE FIRST LITTLE GIFT FOR THEIR CHRISTMAS BOX!

## Wired·up· ornaments

BEGIN WITH A HEART·SHAPE COOKIE CUTTER and A YARD· LONG PIECE OF 18·GAUGE CRAFT WIRE IN SILVER. PRESS THE WIRE AROUND THE COOKIE CUTTER TWICE TO MAKE A HEART SHAPE, THEN REMOVE THE CUTTER. NOW USE LONG PIECES OF COLORED CRAFT WIRE TO "WRAP" THE HEART SHAPE AT RANDOM. TUCK THE WIRE ENDS IN AND TWIST AROUND THE FRAME SO NO LOOSE WIRE ENDS CAN POKE YOU. ATTACH A SATIN RIBBON AT THE TOP AS A HANGER... neat!

## Vickie's good idea:

PUT A SHINY RED JINGLE BELL in THE MIDDLE OF YOUR WIRE ORNAMENT! (OR A PEPPERMINT!)

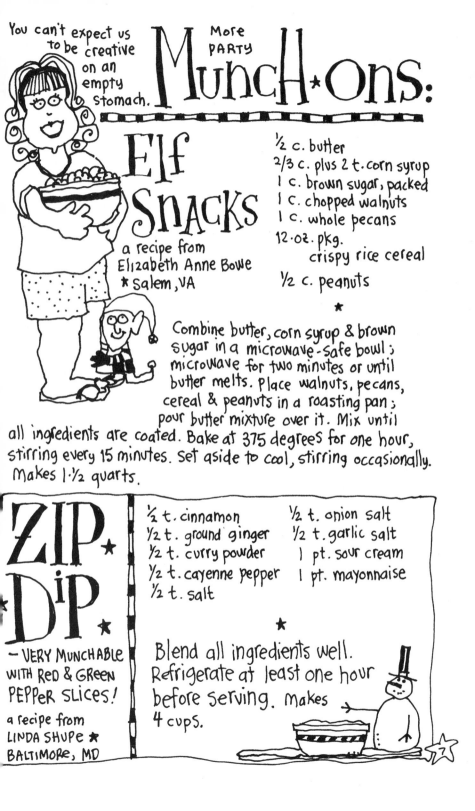

You can't expect us to be creative on an empty stomach.

# More PARTY MuncH*ons:

## Elf Snacks

a recipe from Elizabeth Anne Bowe
★ Salem, VA

½ c. butter
2/3 c. plus 2 t. corn syrup
1 c. brown sugar, packed
1 c. chopped walnuts
1 c. whole pecans
12·oz. pkg. crispy rice cereal
½ c. peanuts

★

Combine butter, corn syrup & brown sugar in a microwave-safe bowl; microwave for two minutes or until butter melts. Place walnuts, pecans, cereal & peanuts in a roasting pan; pour butter mixture over it. Mix until all ingredients are coated. Bake at 375 degrees for one hour, stirring every 15 minutes. Set aside to cool, stirring occasionally. Makes 1·½ quarts.

## ZIP*DiP*

— VERY MUNCHABLE WITH RED & GREEN PEPPER SLICES!

a recipe from LINDA SHUPE ★ BALTIMORE, MD

½ t. cinnamon
½ t. ground ginger
½ t. curry powder
½ t. cayenne pepper
½ t. salt
½ t. onion salt
½ t. garlic salt
1 pt. sour cream
1 pt. mayonnaise

★

Blend all ingredients well. Refrigerate at least one hour before serving. Makes 4 cups.

7

# Bring Ideas in and entertain

Reduce a crayoned Christmas drawing by little Molly and stick it on a stack of adhesive-front refrigerator magnets from the office supply store for all the doting relatives.

Get out your rubber stamp ABCs and personalize a stack of cards & envelopes with a friend's name. Use pretty handmade papers and tie it all together with a neat pen and a beautiful ribbon.

Put an empty mint container to a new use! you know those nice little tin hinged boxes that strong breath mints come in? Simply clean it up and give it a new coat of paint... then glue on little alphabet buttons and old pretty buttons, too, for a great kit for needles and threads. Or rubber-stamp a leaf design and the word "WILDFLOWERS" on top of flat acrylic paint for a seed box!

# them royally, for one of them may be the King.

-MARK VAN DOREN-

## great Little Gifts

"OH · OUR · ACHING · FEET!" your shopping buddies can mix up a healing batch of cooling PEPPERMINT FOOT SCRUB:

2 CUPS SEA SALT IN A PLASTIC BAG WITH A VIAL OF PEPPERMINT ESSENTIAL OIL WILL TUCK RIGHT INTO A STRIPED CHRISTMAS SOCK. TIE THE SOCK SHUT WITH YARN AND ADD A JINGLE BELL and A COPY OF THIS LITTLE TAG. →

### sure ★ fire SHOPPER'S TIRED · TOOTSY ★ CURE ★

MIX ¼ CUP SEA SALT WITH 3 DROPS PEPPERMINT OIL ↺ RUB ON FEET, THEN SOAK IN WARM WATER!

aaaaaaaH.

# great Little gifts with big holiday cheer...

Magic wands might not help, but they surely can't hurt! Find a wand at a party supply store; they're usually silver or gold but you can spray yours red. Dust it liberally with red glitter, and add green sequins or gemstones if you like ↘ add a glittery tag that says,

"Make a Christmas Wish."

Every holiday princess needs one!

Who doesn't need a handy little christmas list pad? Or two? or three? Buy small red spiral-bound notepads and glue on a big green felt star. Add small name strips of paper with glue to give 'em the personal touch.

Kate's Lists

Hmm... I want... and I want... and... I want... and I want... and...

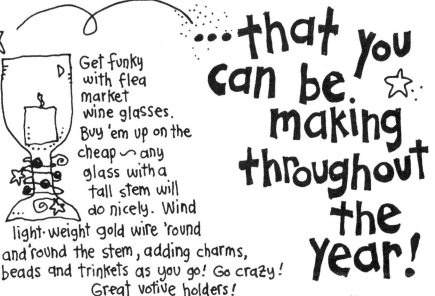

...that you can be making throughout the year!

Get funky with flea market wine glasses. Buy 'em up on the cheap ～ any glass with a tall stem will do nicely. Wind light-weight gold wire 'round and 'round the stem, adding charms, beads and trinkets as you go! Go crazy! Great votive holders!

Decorate these pots in July and you'll be ready to fill them up in December! Use a sponge brush and bright red or white acrylic paint to disguise a plain old clay pot, then use your hot-glue gun to attach peppermints all around the pot's edge. Fill with wrapped Christmas candy come holiday-time!

Use pinking shears to cut out paper labels you've printed on the computer ～ holiday words like "JOY", "NOEL" and "BE MERRY". Glue the labels on pillar candles (rubber bands will keep the labels on while the glue dries) and then gather tulle 'round each pillar to give as a lovely, simple gift.

# Brainstorm a Whole Snowstorm of ideas in July!

BEAT THE HEAT BY THINKING COOL 〜 and WHAT'S COOLER THAN A SNOWMAN? THINK FROSTY THOUGHTS.

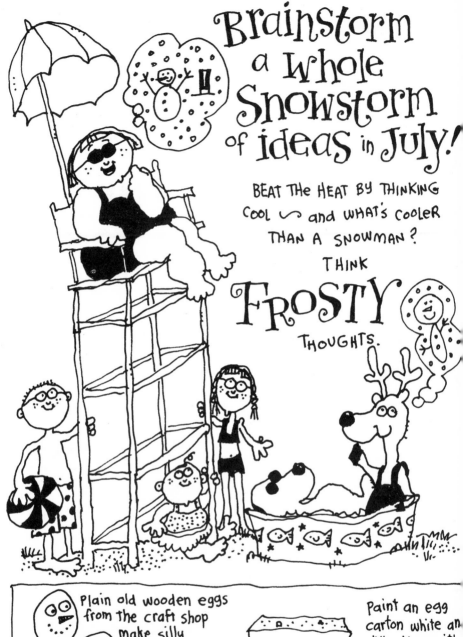

Plain old wooden eggs from the craft shop make silly snowman heads! Paint 'em white, add crazy googly eyes and a big orange nose made of bake-able clay...give one on an egg cup, or by the carton-full!

Paint an egg carton white and glitter it up with a good dusting of clear glitter for a ready-to-give gift box for your showy guys.

When you like your work, everyday is a holiday.

-FRANK TYGER-

Turn your kids loose with cheap extra-large white tee shirts and black fabric markers. Gigantic snowman faces are easy to draw on these over-sized jammie shirts!

QUICK & EASY: Embroider a simple round snowman head on plain white dinner napkins... if you start in July, you can embroider enough for a banquet by December!

Haunt flea markets this summer for old snowman postcards and antique books! You can find both for a song; take the book and alter the old cover by gluing on the postcard. You can add further embellishments like photo corners, charms, glitter... whatever you like! It's a great way to recycle beautiful old cards and books for a snowman lover.

NOEL

# Countdown 'til CHRISTMAS!

Mary Elizabeth is starting early! She's got one big box for each of her best friends, and here's her great idea: She's looking for a very special little gift for each box ∽ one for every day in December, the 1st through the 25th!

The goodies she's hiding inside don't need to be elaborate or expensive ∽ just clever and personal and fun.

Now, to find 25 wonderful little gifts is no small task... but if you start in July, you'll enjoy the thrill of the hunt and you'll have plenty of time to make all sorts of treasures. So follow along as the Country Friends' Christmas boxes fill up...you'll want to start your own stack!

# Doing is the great thing.

—JOHN RUSKIN

**JULY**

## Stock★pile

when you find something cool on sale.

If the thought of 25 gifts is just too **daunting,** here are a couple of twists to the idea:

★ Make your box contain little presents for the **"12 Days of Christmas."**

★ Organize a gift of 25 envelopes, each one with a card, a note, a quotation, a story or a wish inside.

## Silly is good.

Remember that every gift doesn't have to be serious. Inspire giggles with toys, gags and crazy stuff. Whistles, bubble gum, pinwheels & lollipops— we never outgrow 'em.

# GReAt iDeA!

## (BUT I'M BLANK. GIVe Me SOME HINTS.)

Well, for example, take a look at the box of goodies Mary Elizabeth is putting together for her lovable Auntie Ellen. 25 little inexpensive gifts, all wrapped in red and white polka dot paper and packed inside a hat box Mary Elizabeth covered in red and white striped paper. About half the gifts are store-bought, the rest she's made. Each one has a tag marked with, "DO NOT OPEN UNTIL DECEMBER _____!".

Not a one of these little treats cost more than a dollar or two, but Auntie Ellen will think each one precious and dear!

## Now take the iDeA and run!

"I'm Gonna GeT a GIGANTIC Box and PuT in a PONY and Kittens and SPOTTY and a SHOVEL and a BICYCLE and ICE SKATES and a SWING SeT and A SAILBOAT and maybe another PONY and a TURTLE, yeah and a DOLL BUGGY and let's see...."

KEEP A FIRM HAND on the THROTTLE of YOUR CHAIN of THOUGHT. ~ARN GLAS

# Auntie Ellen's Box:

1. Package of bubble bath
2. Silly holiday socks!
3. Teabags in a velvet pouch
4. Candy canes tied with a gingham bow
5. A card with a hand-written holiday poem
6. Photo of Spotty wearing a santa hat
7. christmas notepad & pencil
8. A bag of caramel candy mix
9. Snowman ornament the Kids made
10. Grandma Elsie's recipe for Sugar Cookies on a neat card
11. A teensy little silver star pin
12. Child's old Christmas storybook from a July tag sale
13. A kazoo and a copy of the music to "Frosty the Snowman"!
14. White washcloth embroidered with a holly leaf and soap
15. Peppermints in an antique canning jar
16. Christmas quotation in a garage sale frame
17. A loaf of pumpkin bread IOU, redeemable on demand.
18. A pretty old spoon you know she'll love
19. Homemade potpourri sachets for the car
20. christmas-Red lipstick
21. Glittery green nail polish!
22. A picture of you sitting on Santa's lap ~ good for a giggle!
23. Bayberry votive candle
24. Flavored cocoa mix to leave for Santa
25. An old family Christmas photo in a lovely frame

The glow of one warm thought is to me worth more than money.
- THOMAS JEFFERSON -

SUGAR COOKIES

JOY

# 'Jingle Bells ROCK!

If you've got a little extra change jingling in your pocket, spend it on a bag o' jingle bells!

OH! sew tiny bells on a cheap stocking cap brim, and a big one on top! WHAT FUN!

## Here Birdie, Birdie....

Tie this tag → on a tiny nest from the craft shop and tuck a trio of gold jingle bells inside the nest for a Christmas-time touch.

— Old holiday wisdom —

If a nest in your christmas tree is to be found, Love and good fortune will be yours the year 'round.

Every time you hear these ring, an elf is making Christmas things.

## Elf doorbells:

Buy three pieces of ribbon, each three feet long...red, white & green are nice. Lay them on top of each other, ends sort of matching, and tie them all together at the half-way point. Now tie a bunch of different size jingle bells on the ends of each streamer and add ← this tag!

18

OH MY GLOVES, THEY JINGLE, JANGLE, JINGLE! Sew a pair of BELLS to your MITTENS~ WEAR 'EM ALL CHRISTMAS SEASON OR USE 'EM AS GIFTS ~ JUST TUCK A LITTLE NOTE INSIDE

wishing you **warm hands** and **warm hearts**.

# Jingle Bell Cocoa Mix

a recipe from Becky Kelsoe + Blountsville, AL

3·½ c. Powdered milk
2 c. Powdered sugar
1 c. Unsweetened baking cocoa
1 c. Non-dairy creamer
1 c. Mini marshmallows
½ c. Mini chocolate chips

★

Mix all ingredients together. Place in jars. Makes 9 cups of cocoa mix.

## Jingle Bell Cocoa

Simply mix up ⅓ cup of cocoa blend with 3/4 cup of boiling water and stir well for a yummy mug-full on a snowy day.

You can mix up a big batch of this cocoa well in advance of the holidays... if you store it in airtight jars in a cool, dry cupboard, it will stay fresh up to 8 months. Add this label and jingle bell streamers to gift jars!

* PACK UP AN "H" AND AN "O" COOKIE CUTTER IN A RED GINGHAM BAG ~ TIE IT CLOSED WITH GREEN RIBBON OR RICK-RACK AND THIS HO-HO-HO TAG. (TUCK YOUR FAVORITE SUGAR COOKIE RECIPE IN, TOO!)

Let it HO
Let it HO
Let it HO-HO-HO

* ADD A CHEERY LITTLE TAG TO A CUTE HOLIDAY SPREADER FOR YOUR FAVORITE GOURMET.

I LIKE TO Spread a Little Cheer this time of year!

Set me a task in which I can put something of my very Self, and it is a task no longer; it is JOY; it is Art.
— BLISS CARMAN —

20

COOL! now where are the cheese & crackers?

★ FIND SOME FUN, OLD-FASHIONED MEASURING CUPS OR MEASURING SPOONS. TIE ON A TAG LIKE THIS ONE ↓

★ idea!
Fill your measuring cups with tiny bags of oh·so·fragrant

wishing you all
J ★ O ★ Y
Beyond measure!

# Winter Spice Potpourri

Make a batch in July and keep it in a dry, cool spot until December!

a recipe from Kim Brown ★ Goodrich, MI

10 oranges
8 lemons
20 Bay leaves, crumbled
20 cinnamon sticks, coarsely broken

1 c. whole cloves
1 c. whole allspice

Add ¼ cup of winter spice potpourri to a pot of simmering water and enjoy the scent!

Peel skins from fruit using a potato peeler, leaving the white pith on the fruit. Set fruit aside for use in another recipe. Tear peels into one-inch pieces; arrange in a single layer on baking sheets. Bake at 175 degrees for 1·½ hours, stirring occasionally. Remove from oven; let air-dry for at least 24 hours. Place peels in a mixing bowl; add remaining ingredients, gently tossing to mix. Store in an airtight container.
← Attach instructions.

21

# Make Ahead Goodies

KICK OFF YOUR FLIP-FLOPS and CHECK INTO THE KITCHEN THIS SUMMER FOR EARLY CHRISTMAS COOKIN'!

## Vickie's Peanut Butter Cup Cookies in a Jar

...make ahead for gifts! Mix will stay fresh for 6 months!

3/4 c. SUGAR
1/4 c. BROWN SUGAR, PACKED
1.3/4 c. ALL-PURPOSE FLOUR
1 t. BAKING POWDER
1/2 t. BAKING SODA
8 PEANUT BUTTER CUPS, COARSELY CHOPPED

Layer the first five ingredients listed in a one-quart, wide-mouth jar; firmly pack each layer before adding the next. Set aside. Place peanut butter cups in a plastic zipping bag; tuck on top of mix. Secure lid and attach the instructions.

## Peanut Butter Cups in a Jar Cookie Mix

Remove candy pieces from jar; set aside. Add mix to a large mixing bowl; toss gently with a fork to mix. Add 1/2 cup softened butter, one slightly beaten egg and one teaspoon vanilla extract; blend well. Fold in candy pieces; form dough into walnut-size balls. Arrange on lightly greased baking sheets and bake at 375 degrees for 12 to 14 minutes. Cool for 5 minutes on the baking sheets, then remove to wire racks to cool completely. Makes 2 1/2 dozen.

## Coffee STIR * STICKS

a recipe from Flo Burtnett
* GAGE, OK

Brew up a fragrant batch of these, then store them in an airtight container until Christmas rolls around ～ they'll stay fresh up to 8 months.

* ✱ *

1 c. sugar
⅓ c. brewed coffee
1 T. corn syrup
¼ t. baking cocoa
¼ t. cinnamon
½ t. vanilla extract
12 lollipop or craft sticks

* ✱ *

Combine sugar, coffee, syrup, cocoa and cinnamon in a saucepan. Heat over medium heat until sugar dissolves, stirring occasionally. Continue heating over medium heat, without stirring, until mixture reaches 290 degrees on a candy thermometer. Remove from heat; immediately stir in vanilla. Pour tablespoons of mixture into circles on a greased jelly-roll pan; insert the top ½-inch of a lollipop stick into each circle. Allow to cool until hardened. Wrap each stirrer in plastic wrap and tie with a ribbon. Makes about one dozen.

## STIR STICK

STIR YOUR COFFEE WITH THIS CANDY FOR A CUPPA BREW THAT TASTES JUST **DANDY!**

⌐ attach a COPY OF THIS TAG TO EACH STIRRER!

Better three Hours too soon than one minute too late.

- WILLIAM SHAKESPEARE -

# JoAnn's Lollies

OLD-FASHIONED CANDY WE'VE NEVER OUTGROWN!

# How Sweet it is!

1.½ c. SUGAR
½ c. WATER
8 TO 12 DROPS FOOD COLORING
1 t. DESIRED FLAVORED EXTRACT
LOLLIPOP STICKS

♥

Combine sugar and water in a heavy saucepan; heat over medium-high heat 'til sugar dissolves, about one to two minutes. Continue heating until it boils; cover and heat for three minutes. Uncover and heat until mixture reaches 310 degrees on a candy thermometer; remove from heat. Carefully stir in food coloring and flavoring; pour into lollipop molds. Insert sticks; cool for 20 to 25 minutes. Remove from molds; transfer to parchment paper-lined baking sheets to cool.

Makes 2 cups syrup. Quantity of lollipops depends on your candy mold.

Make a lollipop bouquet!

# Share the love at Christmas·time

## ... And

### THE COUNTRY FRIENDS'

# Hard Tack Candy!

2 c. SUGAR
3/4 c. CORN SYRUP
1 c. HOT WATER

FOOD COLORING
1/2 t. FLAVORED EXTRACT

*

Combine ingredients in a heavy saucepan and cook to 300 degrees on a candy thermometer. Add drops of food coloring to desired tint, then add flavored extract (we like cinnamon, clove and peppermint!). Pour out on a marble slab; cut with scissors as soon as the candy is cool enough to handle. Store in an airtight container.

Idea! PACK YOUR HARD TACK IN CLEAN BABY FOOD JARS WITH SPRAY-PAINTED LIDS ~ GLUE ON A COPY OF THIS FUN LITTLE CHRISTMAS LABEL!

# Summer

...the season
of inferior
sledding.
—Eskimo proverb—

merry christmas from

25

# G*r*e*a*t GUY G*I*F*T*S

GOOD IDEAS FOR THE NOTORIOUSLY·HARD·TO·BUY·FOR MEN ON YOUR CHRISTMAS LIST.

# car cologne

You know those scent sachets you can buy that come in paper envelopes? Personalize 'em for great guys' stocking stuffers: simply find an old family photo and copy it on the right·hand side of an 8½"×11" piece of paper, like this. Now fold the paper in half, like this.

Glue or sew along the sides and bottom to make an envelope — leave the top open.

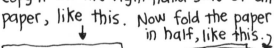

Now slip the scent sachet in the new envelope you've made and sew or glue the top shut ⌒ all done! (A couple of fun ideas: find a family photo of Uncle Bill with his 1925 Model T and write "Everybody loves a guy with a cool car" on the envelope! Or put a cinnamon roll scent in an envelope with Grandma's picture on it!)

# Frame of Fame

Turn a plain old wooden frame into a treasure for someone special! Take copies of favorite photographs of Grandpa, for instance; a shot of him with the grandkids, one by the family home, some action shots at the lake with the babies. Set aside.

Every family needs a Grandpa Joe.

Sand a flat wooden frame with fairly wide molding and dust well, then paint a creamy color and let it dry. Give it an aged look with a coat of light stain if you like. Let it dry completely. Arrange the photos in a pleasing way on the frame, letting them overlap. Cut to size ∽ you might want to use deckle-edged craft scissors to make the photo edges more "soft" and interesting.

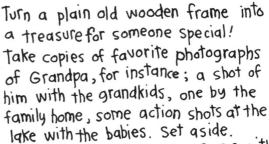

Now glue the photos in place with decoupage medium, making sure they are flat and smooth. Apply a coat or two of water-based varnish to all surfaces and let dry.

The last step: hand-letter or use a rubber stamp alphabet to write out an appropriate quotation to put inside the frame before you give it away ∽ he'll love the gift and the giver.

## Junk★Food★25★Day★ Extravaganza!

to TONY

It's not healthful but it's well-loved ∽ give your favorite guy a big bucket stuffed with chips, dips, candy bars, beef jerky, bubble gum, pork rinds. When all else fails, you can't go wrong with a gift to eat. (Don't forget the antacids.)

CHIPOS  COLA

# A HAPPY PACK!

* Sew two dishtowels together to make a bag ~ trim with ribbons or rickrack, and fill the bag with gifts.

* Two big, soft bathtowels can be sewn together into a gift sack ~ take it to a monogram shop and have a name embroidered on it just for fun.

* Tuck teeny packages into mateless mittens.

OK, you've made a giant pile of great little gifts ~ now what? Pack 'em up with style!

Mary Elizabeth

Kate

A LITTLE BOX WITH BIG STYLE:
* Wrap little gifts in plain brown kraft paper or shiny red foil wrap ~ then glue on a copy of a little tag and little old buttons.

* CARDBOARD ROLLS FROM WRAPPING PAPER or PAPER TOWELS can be recycled into cool Christmas "Crackers". Cut the tube to an appropriate length and wrap it up with layers of patterned tissue. Pop a little gift inside and tie the ends shut with tinsel or streamers!

Peace

★ Merry ★ Christmas

merry * Christmas

a Surprise Package just for you!

* you know those round tags with metal rims you can buy at the office supply store? They make unique gift tags and package decorations ~ stamp a star or an initial on one, or glue a photo on the tag! Use hotglue to attach an old bead, charm or game piece to one for a one-of-a-kind keeper.

# Jo Ann's TAG STORE

Feel free to come in and make copies of these holiday tags ~ glad to be of service!

Don't Open until December

WELCOME

SPECIAL DELIVERY:
SANTA, please deliver on DECEMBER

wait 'til December

E very man is worth just as much as the things he busies himself with

—MARCUS AURELIUS ANTONINUS

# 15
# THINGS to TUCK
## inside a
# CHRISTMAS CARD

Cash

a book of stamps

37

a Paper snowflake

a neat bookmark

button magnets

a tiny heart snipped from an old quilt

A Friend is a Second self. -CICERO-

a favorite quotation

Wish you were here!

a special Wish

a felt coaster

a paper dolly with a photo of your friend's face glued on!

THINK OF ME

a teabag with a special tag attached

Stickers!

a favorite vintage photo

PIZZA SHUTTLE COUPON

Gift certificates for a yummy treat

Pretty Hair Ribbons

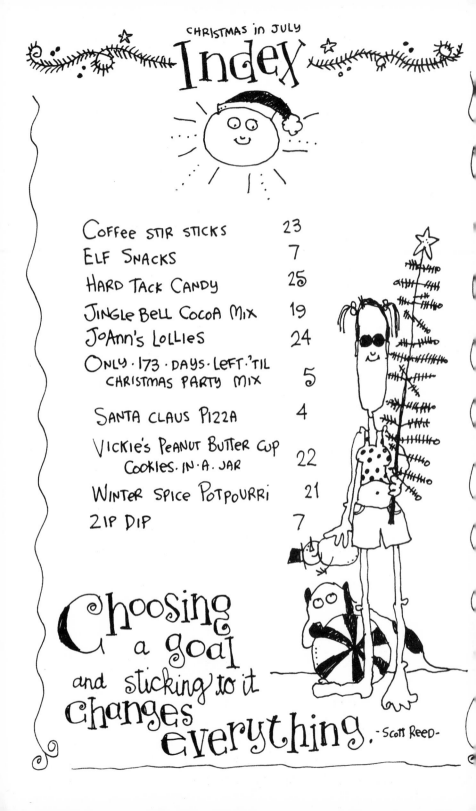

CHRISTMAS IN JULY
# Index

Choosing a goal and sticking to it changes everything. —SCOTT REED—